First published in Great Britain in 2011 by Buster Books,
an imprint of Michael O'Mara Books Limited,
9 Lion Yard, Tremadoc Road, London SW4 7NQ

Written by Katherine Hodges
Illustrated by Katy Jackson with additional illustrations by Nellie Ryan,
Tom Sperling, Lyn Stone/The Art Agency, Dusan Pavlic and Ruth Galloway
Production by Joanne Rooke
Edited by Liz Scoggins and Katherine Hodges
Designed by Zoe Quayle
Cover based on an original design by www.blacksheep-uk.com
Cover illustration by Paul Moran

A CIP catalogue record for this book is available from the British Library

ISBN: 978-1-907151-76-7

2 4 6 8 10 9 7 5 3 1

www.mombooks.com/busterbooks

This book was printed in July 2011 by L.E.G.O., Viale dell'Industria 2, 36100, Vicenza, Italy.

MIX
Paper from
responsible sources
FSC® C023419
www.fsc.org

By buying products with an FSC label you are supporting the growth of responsible forest management worldwide. Papers used by Michael O'Mara Books are natural, recyclable products made from wood grown in sustainable forests. The manufacturing processes conform to the environmental regulations of the country of origin.

The GIRLS' Annual 2012

Buster Books

Contents

Hey There, Sister!

All About You

Tasty Treats

Fun With Friends

Super Stories

Marvellous Makes

Brilliant Brain-teasers

Nifty Knowledge

Answers

Hey There, Sister!

Being a girl today is great
because the world is at your feet and
with this fantastic annual packed full of things
to do, you can unleash your creative side
and make all your dreams come true.

There are super stories to read and brain-teasers
to boggle at. Test your knowledge with the cool quizzes
and use the fab flowcharts to find out more
about yourself. Have a laugh with friends
by playing some great new games,
then make some sweet treats to enjoy together.

The best thing about being a girl
is that you can be made of sugar and spice
and all things nice, but also have
style and spirit and wisdom and wit.

Whatever your interests, you're sure to
have fun with this awesome annual,
so let's get cracking!

Sugar Cookies

These delicious lemon sugar cookies are perfect for a picnic. Use cookie cutters to create fantastic shapes, or save time and simply bake tablespoon-sized dollops of the mixture for equally tasty round cookies.

1. Blend the butter, sugar and salt together using a wooden spoon.

2. Grate the zest from the lemon and add it to the mixture.

3. Combine the flour, baking powder and bicarbonate of soda. Then add the egg and mix thoroughly.

4. Chill the dough in the fridge for half an hour while you lightly grease some baking trays. Preheat the oven to 200 °C/Gas mark 6.

WARNING:
Ask an adult to help you when you use the oven.

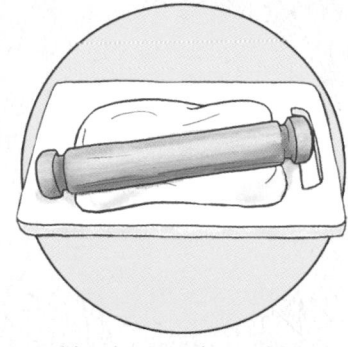

5. Sprinkle the work surface with flour and roll out the cookie dough so that it's about 5 mm thick.

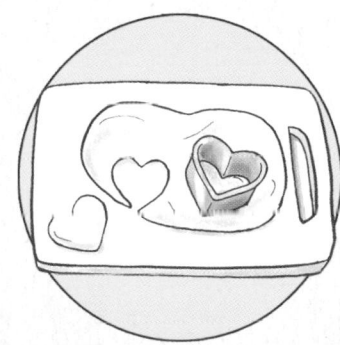

6. Use a cookie cutter to press out your sugar cookies. They will rise quite a lot as they bake, so simple outlines will work better. Sprinkle nutmeg and sugar on top before you put the cookies in the oven.

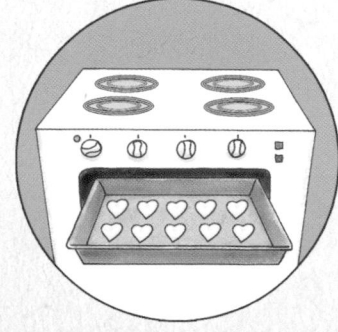

7. Bake the cookies for approximately 8 –10 minutes until they are a light golden colour.

You Will Need:

✳ 100 g unsalted butter

✳ 175 g caster sugar, plus extra for sprinkling

✳ ½ tsp salt

✳ 1 lemon

✳ 275 g flour

✳ 1 tsp baking powder

✳ ½ tsp bicarbonate of soda

✳ 1 egg

✳ grated nutmeg

8. Pop on oven gloves and take the cookies out of the oven. Leave them to cool. Don't be tempted to try to eat them while they are too hot!

Find Your Soul Colour

Use this handy quiz to find the colour that best reflects you.
Start in the middle and just follow the arrows flowing outwards.

Red Divas are energetic, ambitious and bold – real livewires. They are adventurous, exciting and can be quite passionate.

Pink Ladies are charming, sociable, and have a taste for the finer things in life. They also tend to be incurable romantics.

Purple Princesses are sensitive sweeties with a few very close friends. They are creative with a great sense of humour.

White Souls are lovely dreamers and loyal friends. They're very organized and hate it when things don't go to plan.

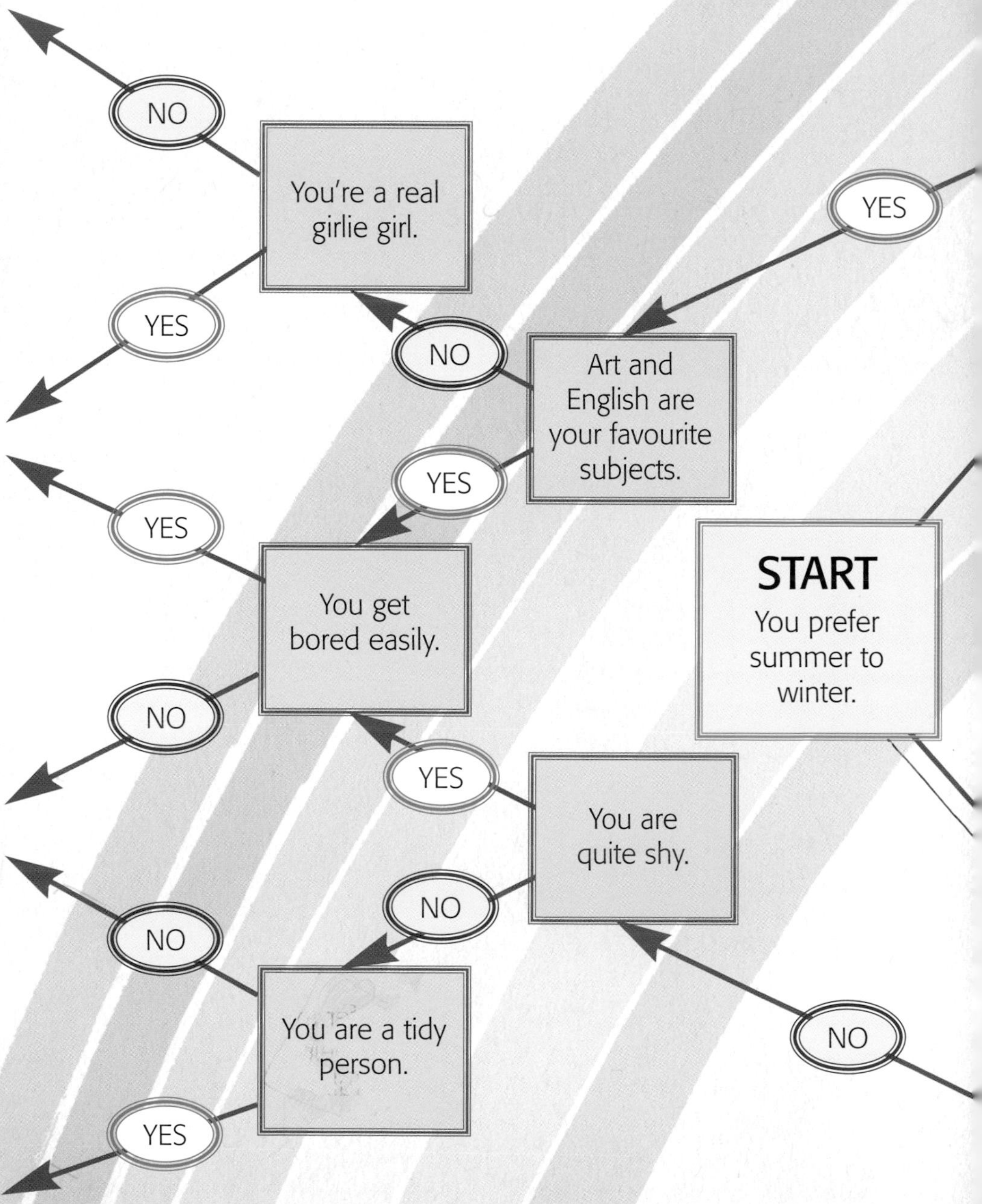

NO

You're a real girlie girl.

YES

YES

NO

Art and English are your favourite subjects.

YES

YES

You get bored easily.

START
You prefer summer to winter.

NO

YES

You are quite shy.

NO

NO

You are a tidy person.

NO

YES

DID YOU KNOW?

In the Jain religion, which began in India, the colour of the soul is said to indicate a person's spiritual progress. Envy, spite and dishonesty give souls a very dull or extremely harsh colour. However, good will and selflessness give souls a pleasing hue and the fragrance of sweet flowers.

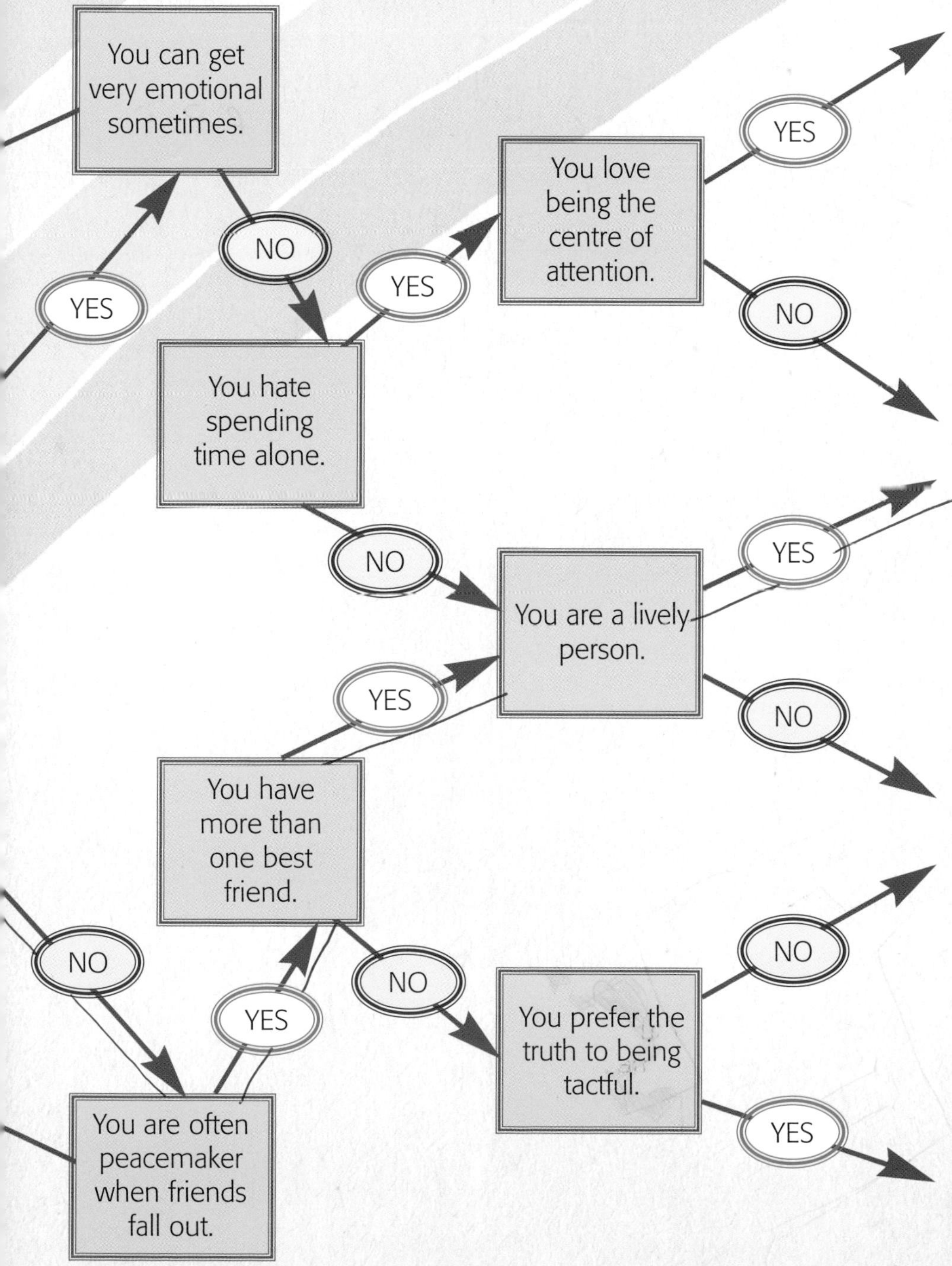

You can get very emotional sometimes.

YES

NO

YES

You hate spending time alone.

You love being the centre of attention.

YES

NO

NO

You are a lively person.

YES

NO

YES

You have more than one best friend.

NO

YES

NO

You prefer the truth to being tactful.

NO

YES

NO

You are often peacemaker when friends fall out.

Orange Sisters are social butterflies – popular and fun-loving. They are confident, chatty and the life of any party.

Yellow Lovelies are friendly, funny and like to try new things. They are bright, inquisitive, and always on the go.

Green Girls are kind, generous and get along well with people. They are chilled, fair-minded and can think for themselves.

Blue Babes are cool, confident and responsible. They are intelligent and have the bravery to stand up for their beliefs.

Riddles Of The Sphinx

Sphinxes are known for setting some puzzling riddles. Can you solve all of these brilliant Egyptian brain-teasers? The answers are on page 60.

BEAUTY MINDBUSTER

Use the key to translate Cleopatra's beauty secret.

A
B
C
D
F
G
H

I
K
L
M
N
O
P

R
S
T
U
W
Y

A · DAILY
BATH · IN
MILK · for
SOFT · SKIN

PYRAMID PUZZLER

Help Amnatra find her way through the pyramid to the treasure. Watch out for snakes and mummies!

START

SNEAKY SCARABS *C and E*

Which two scarab beetles are identical?

KING TUT'S TOMB

There are 5 differences between these two masks.
Can you spot them all?

SPHINX SUDOKU

Complete the grid so that there is one of each of the hieroglyphs in each row, column and box.

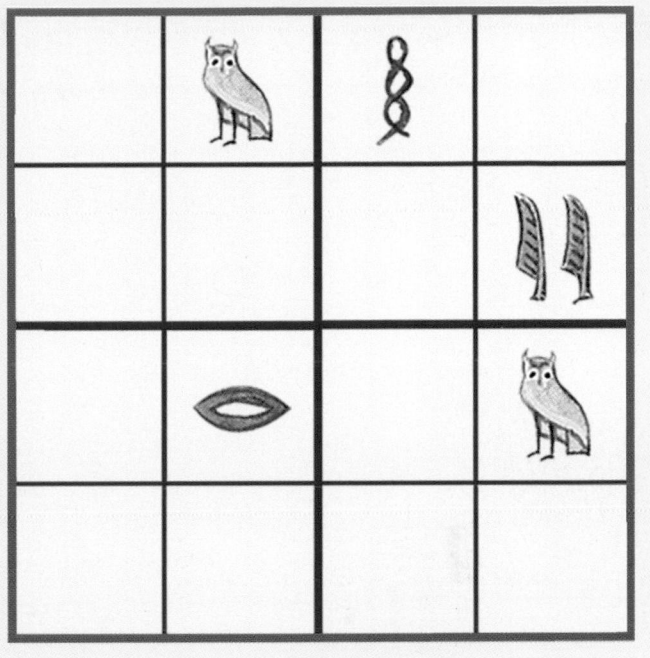

RIDDLE ME THIS

used answers

Most people will have seen pictures of Egypt's Sphinx – a mythical creature with the head of a human and the body of a lion. Did you know the ancient Greeks had a sphinx, too? According to legend, she set travellers riddles. Those who couldn't answer were killed. Try some of these riddles to see if you would have passed her tricky test!

1. What is invisible and only speaks when spoken to? *An echo*

2. What does everyone await though it has never been seen and will never arrive? *Tomorrow*

3. What do you want to share when you have it, but you cease to have once you share it? *A secret*

4. What goes through a door but never enters or leaves? *A keyhole*

5. What is neither big nor small, not solid, not liquid nor gas, and yet can be broken without being dropped? *Silence*

Football Hero

Amy was awesome at football, the only problem was getting to play.

'Guess what, Amy, there's going to be a big match in the park later,' said Matt, as the two of them were walking to school together. 'Meadow Hill versus St Nick's. I hope we win!'

Matt and Amy were next door neighbours, but they were also close friends and massive football fans. They both went to Meadow Hill School and, like everyone there, they longed to see the kids from St Nicholas' School get a pasting on the football pitch.

The two of them walked into the playground. All the boys in their year were huddled together with Dan at the centre of the group. He seemed to have become the self-appointed captain of the team.

A FRIENDSHIP TESTED

'Right, so Matt's in goal, Tom's on the wing, and Nikesh is in midfield,' said Dan. 'Then I think we'll have Sam, Phillip and me as our strikers.'

'What position am I playing, Dan?' asked Amy.

Dan laughed as if she'd said something funny, and carried on talking. 'Eric, Shane, you're defending –'

'Dan!' said Amy more loudly. 'What am I doing?'

'You can stand on the sidelines and cheer us on with the rest of the girls,' said Dan.

'What?' shouted Amy. 'You're not letting me play?'

'What makes you think we'd want a girl on our team?' Dan sneered.

Amy looked at Matt, who had been her friend for years. Surely he wasn't going to side with the other boys? Matt squirmed and looked away.

'Sorry, Amy,' he mumbled. 'But it looks like the team's already been chosen.'

'Well, thanks a lot!' Amy snapped. She was annoyed because she knew without being big-headed that she could dribble the ball past her opponents more nimbly than Phillip, could run faster than Tom and could kick harder and further than Dan. Why couldn't they just give her a chance?

'That's the most ridiculous thing I've ever heard,' said Amy's best friend Vanisha when she told her about it at lunch break. 'So Dan won't let you play just because you're a girl, even though you're brilliant?'

'No, but I'll go along just to see what happens,' Amy replied. 'Anyway, they might need someone to explain the offside rule to them.'

LEFT OUT OF THE TEAM

The last lesson of the day was Geography. Amy was trying to listen as Miss Hobbes droned on about earthquakes. But all she could think about was the upcoming match.

When the bell rang she packed away her things and left before Matt could catch up with her. She walked to the park on her own. Some of the St Nick's kids were already there in their navy blue jumpers, kicking a ball about. Amy threw down her bag and joined in.

'Hey, Hilly,' shouted a blond boy, noticing her red Meadow Hill top. 'Are your lot so desperate they're letting girls play?'

Amy ignored him and concentrated on the ball.

'Wow, she's good!' someone else said.

'And we're even better,' called Dan as he dumped his bag on the sidelines.

Together, the students threw down jumpers for goalposts and persuaded an older boy from Castle School to act as referee. As the ref whistled and the game began, Meadow Hill looked promising. They moved briskly up the pitch and nearly scored a few times. But St Nick's were better than they looked, and before Meadow Hill knew what was happening, they had managed to seize the ball and boot it past Matt.

'Goal!' shouted St Nick's.

'Right,' Dan roared, an ugly expression on his face. 'Let's show them what we're made of!'

DESPERATE DAN

Meadow Hill team were playing aggressively, desperate to even the score. Dan suddenly dived forward, slipped, and fell heavily on his ankle. It was horrible. Dan's face was a ghostly white as he tried to stand.

'I'm fine,' he said. 'Just give me a minute.'

'No way,' said the ref. 'You shouldn't even be walking on that.'

'But the match …' said Dan desperately.

'Meadow Hill will just have to play a man down,' the ref said.

Amy, who had been glumly watching the match's progress nearby, stepped forward.

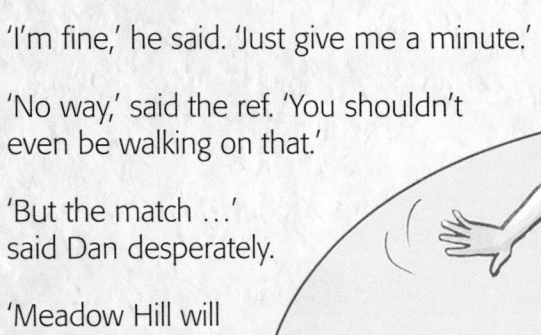

'I could sub in, I'm all warmed up,' said Amy. 'It wouldn't be fair if our side were a player short.'

'All right, fine,' said the referee. There was some disgruntled muttering. 'Does anyone have a problem with that? Good.'

Amy ran on to the the pitch. She saw the blond St Nick's boy coming towards her with the ball and nimbly tackled him. She passed to Nikesh, who passed back, and she passed to Sam. They were working together seamlessly, and soon they were bearing down on the goal. A minute later, Sam had scored an equalizer.

A RISKY KICK

The teams played on, even though it was starting to rain. There were some close runs, but neither team scored again.

'One minute to go!' shouted the ref.

With the rain pelting down, Amy and the Meadow Hill boys raced up the pitch, passing the ball. Knowing that they would never make it down the field in time, Amy made a risky decision. She summoned all her strength and gave the ball an almighty kick towards the goal. Her hopes rose within her as she watched it sail down the field in a glorious arc. The St Nick's goalkeeper dived for it, missed, and the ball rolled between the two navy-blue jumpers making their goal.

The match was over, and they had won!

VICTORY

Ten boys in red tops rushed towards Amy. They picked her up and carried her on their shoulders, chanting her name.

'We won! We won!' Matt kept saying.

'All thanks to Amy!' exclaimed Sam.

Dan was sitting next to the pitch looking pale but overjoyed, in spite of his puffy ankle.

'Good game,' said the blond boy as they left. 'How about a rematch next week?'

'Only if Amy can play,' said Matt.

'Yeah,' said Dan, as he hopped along beside them, his arm around Sam's neck for support. 'She's our best player!'

Origami Tulips

All you need to make a pretty flower are two squares of paper of the same size, one pink and one green. Make as many as you like to create a beautiful paper bouquet.

MAKING THE FLOWER HEAD

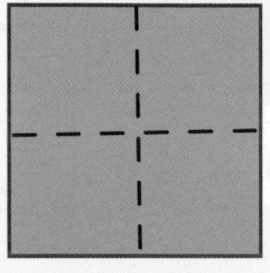
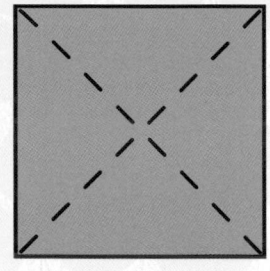
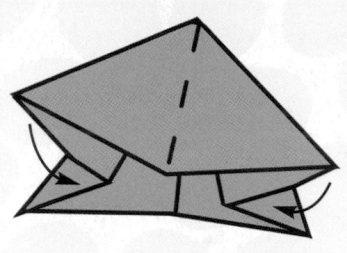

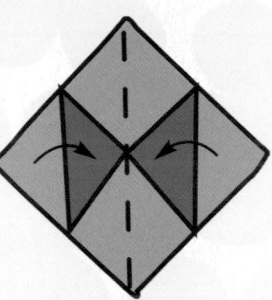

1. Fold the square of paper down the middle in both directions.

2. Unfold the paper, then fold in half down both diagonals.

3. Bring two of the facing sides in together along the creases to make a diamond shape.

4. Turn the diamond shape so that the open end is at the top.

5. Fold the side corners of the top layer across to the centre line.

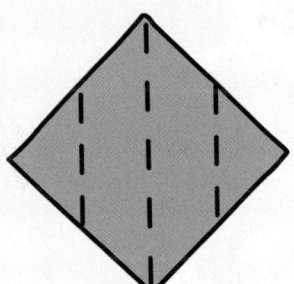

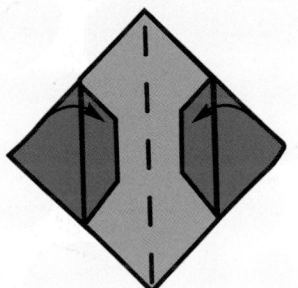

6. Unfold, leaving a crease.

7. Fold the side corners of the top layer across to the new crease.

8. Fold each side over again towards the centre.

9. Turn your paper over and repeat steps **5** to **8** until you end up with the shape shown above.

10. Fold the lower edges of the top layer to the centre line.

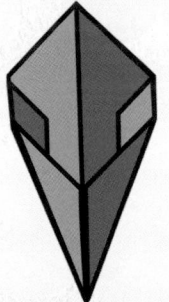
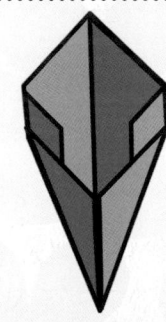
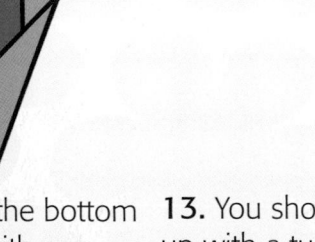
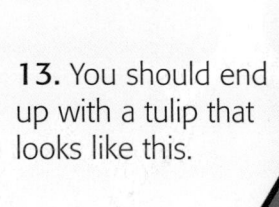
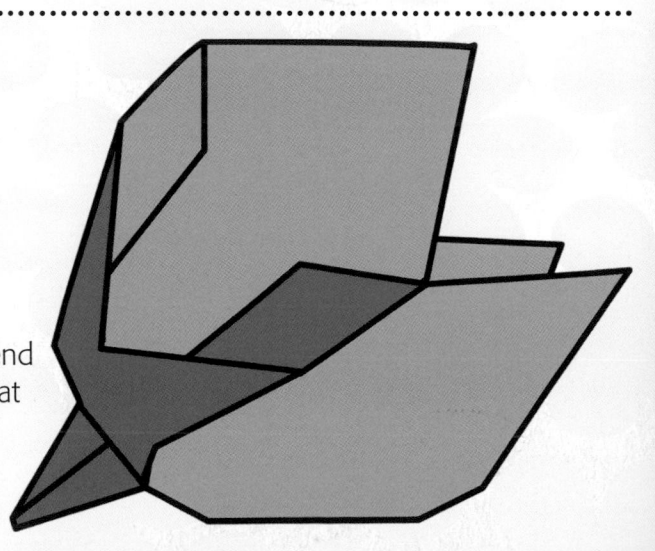

11. Turn the flower over and repeat step **10** on the other side.

12. Holding the bottom of the tulip with one hand, gently open the petals at the top.

13. You should end up with a tulip that looks like this.

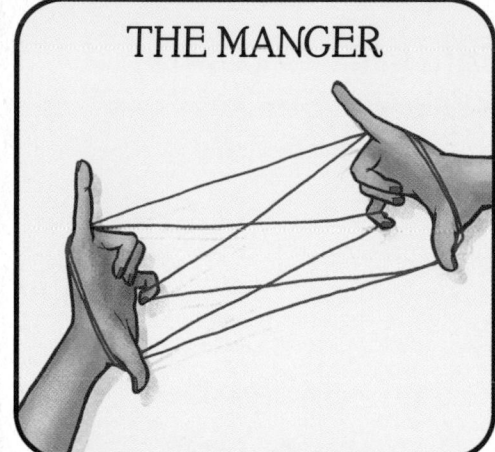

THE MANGER

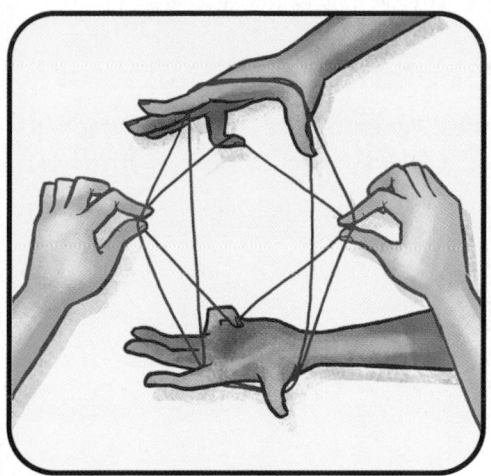

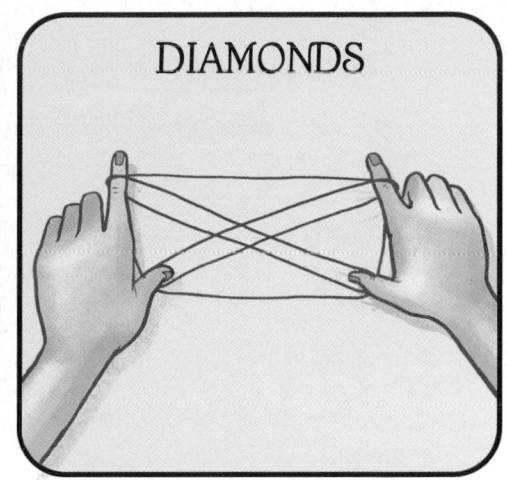

DIAMONDS

7. Your friend should pull her hands tight, keeping the string hooked over her little fingers. This forms The Manger, or Reverse Cradle.

8. Pinch your fingers and thumbs together round the crosses from underneath. Bring your hands out and over the outer string and pull them tight.

9. Diamonds is a reverse Soldier's Bed, so your fingers and thumbs point down. Your friend should perform step **4**, bringing the crosses over the string and your hands back up through the centre.

THE CAT'S EYE

FISH IN A DISH

10. She should get this pattern, the Cat's Eye. To continue the game, pick up the diagonal string with your little finger where it loops round the outer strings and repeat the action you used for Candles. You should end up with The Manger.

11. To finish the game from the Cat's Eye formation, put your forefingers and thumbs down through each of the triangles and scoop up them up through the centre. Pull your hands apart to create this shape, the Fish In A Dish.

Hollywood Bingo

Ask a couple of friends round to play a game or two of Hollywood Bingo. Two budding actresses are vying with each other for stardom, but who has what it takes to be the next big thing? Play the game and find out!

1. Choose one player to be the 'Presenter', while the other two are the 'Actresses'.

2. The two Actresses then choose a clapperboard and matching counters, which they should cut out carefully.

3. Without letting the Presenter see, the Actresses should each choose nine different objects from the counters, placing them face up on their clapperboards.

4. The Presenter should then call out objects from the list in a random order, preferably in a dramatic awards-ceremony voice.

5. Each time the Presenter says the name of an item that an Actress has on her clapperboard, she must hand the item to the Presenter.

6. The first Actress to clear all the items from her clapperboard and shout 'Lights, camera, action!' is the winner.

1. Oscar
2. Shoes
3. Shopping bag
4. Comb
5. Microphone
6. Milkshake
7. Movie camera
8. Nail varnish
9. Sunglasses
10. Rose
11. Fan mail
12. Dog
13. Private jet
14. Palm tree
15. Key to mansion
16. Flip-flop
17. Stretch limo
18. Hairdryer
19. Dress
20. Brush
21. Postcard
22. Sundae
23. Purse
24. Lipstick

Hollywood Glamour

Shine like a superstar with these top beauty tips.

SUPER BODY SCRUB

Exfoliating helps to remove dead skin cells and gives your skin a fresh, glowing look. Use a flannel to carefully massage a few tablespoons of sea salt across the surface of your skin. Avoid sensitive areas like the skin around your eyes. Don't do this more than once a week as your skin needs time to renew itself.

FABULOUS FACE MASK

You can make your own face mask quite cheaply and easily by mixing together a tablespoon of oatmeal, a tablespoon of live, organic yogurt and a few drops of honey. Cleanse your face before applying the mask and make sure your hair is tied back out of the way. Apply the mixture with your fingertips, avoiding the sensitive skin around your eyes. Leave for ten minutes, then wash it off to admire your clean and glowing skin.

TOP TIP:

Scrubbing your nails with whitening toothpaste will take away stains and leave you with brilliantly bright nails. Use some clear top coat to finish them off.

MOVIE STAR NAILS

Invite a friend round and give each other luxury manicures.

Here's what to do:

1. Make sure that you take off any old nail varnish with a ball of cotton wool soaked in nail polish remover.

2. Soak your hands in warm water for about ten minutes. Then use a wooden cuticle stick to push back your cuticles – the tough layer of skin at the base of each nail. Never cut them as this can lead to infection.

3. Trim your nails with nail scissors and file the ends smooth in a curved motion with an emery board.

4. Apply a base coat of clear nail varnish so that the colour glides on smoothly. It will also help to avoid deep colours staining.

5. Choose a colour and paint your nails, using as few strokes of the brush as possible. Add extra coats if needed.

6. Finally, apply a clear top coat for a professional finish.

Behind The Scenes

The costume department can get very busy in between takes. Can you spot the ten differences in these two scenes? The answers are on page 60.

Movie Magic Quiz

How well do you know your film facts? Check your answers on page 60.

1. In Tim Burton's film *Charlie and the Chocolate Factory*, why is Willy Wonka so obsessed with sweets?

a. He has never eaten savoury foods.
b. His dentist father wouldn't let him eat sweets as a child.
c. A talking jelly bean once told him that he would be the best sweet-maker in the world.

2. What is the name of Justin Bieber's first film?

a. *Never Say Never*
b. *Always Say Forever*
c. *Never Say Haircut*

3. Which of the following is not a character in the Disney version of *Snow White and the Seven Dwarfs*?

a. Smiley
b. Bashful
c. Sneezy

4. In *Gnomeo and Juliet*, where do Gnomeo and Juliet first meet?

a. At a fancy dress party
b. In another garden
c. At a lawnmower race

5. What is the name of Johnny Depp's character in *Pirates of the Caribbean*?

a. Jack Swan
b. Jack Starling
c. Jack Sparrow

6. What disease is everyone afraid of catching in *Diary of a Wimpy Kid*?

a. The boogie woogie flu
b. The cheese touch
c. The dreaded lurgy

7. How many other nannies have Cecil Brown's family driven away before Nanny McPhee arrives?

a. 5
b. 12
c. 17

8. What is the name of the boy who owns the toys in the *Toy Story* films?

a. Andy
b. Ben
c. Chris

9. What type of lizard is Rango?

a. Iguana
b. Gecko
c. Chameleon

10. In *Kung Fu Panda*, where does Po work before he becomes a kung fu fighter?

a. A fortune cookie factory
b. His family's noodle shop
c. A computer repair centre

Rock On!

Add some rock'n'roll glamour to your wardrobe by customizing a T-shirt. Here are four fantastic ways to make a unique top of your very own.

BEAUTIFUL BOWS

Snip small slits along the neck, hem and sleeves of your T-shirt. Thread some satin ribbon through the slits and finish off by tying the ends in a bow.

SUPER-COOL SEAMS

Cut the side seams from the bottom of the T-shirt to under the arms. Measure the side seam and mark four equally spaced points along the length about 2 cm from the edge. Make a hole at each point, making sure it goes though both pieces of fabric. Thread ribbons or laces through the holes and tie them into bows.

STUNNING STENCILS

Make a stencil by cutting your chosen shape out of card. Pin the stencil to your T-shirt and apply fabric paint with a sponge. Carefully remove the stencil to reveal your design. When the fabric paint is dry, get an adult to iron the design according to the instructions on the paint pot.

RIOTOUS RIPS

Get the punk look by cutting slits down the front of a T-shirt and wearing it over a top in a contrasting colour.

Ballet Boggler

These ballerinas have been busy rehearsing Swan Lake. Can you spot the eight differences between the two performances? Check your answers on page 60.

Butterfly Cakes

These cute little cakes are fun to make and are the perfect treat to serve at any tea party. Make the classic red and white version below, or go wild and decorate them with food colouring, small sweets and silver balls.

You Will Need:

For the cakes:
* ✳ 100 g butter
* ✳ 100 g caster sugar
* ✳ 2 eggs
* ✳ 100 g self-raising flour
* ✳ 1 tsp vanilla essence
* ✳ 12 cake cases

To decorate:
* ✳ 50 g butter at room temperature
* ✳ 100 g icing sugar
* ✳ glacé cherries

WARNING:
Ask an adult to help you when you use the oven.

1. Preheat the oven to 190 °C /Gas mark 5 and place the paper cases in the cupcake tin.

2. Beat the butter and sugar together with a wooden spoon until it's fluffy and creamy.

3. In a separate bowl, thoroughly beat the eggs with the vanilla essence. Add the egg, a little at a time, to the butter and sugar.

4. Sift in the flour a little at a time, stirring it in thoroughly as you go.

5. Half-fill the paper cases with cake mixture. You should be able to make about a dozen cakes.

6. Put the cupcake tin into the oven for 15 – 20 minutes. When the cakes are golden, insert a toothpick. If it comes away clean, they are ready.

7. When the cakes are cool enough to touch, they can be lifted out of the cupcake tin and placed on a wire rack to cool completely.

HOW TO TRANSFORM YOUR CUPCAKES INTO BUTTERFLY CAKES

1. Ask an adult to cut a small circle off the top of each cake with a sharp knife. Cut the circles in half and put them to one side.

2. Mix together the butter and the icing sugar. Pop it into the hollow on top of the cakes.

3. Push the two halves of the cake circles into the icing, with the baked tops facing up towards each other, so they look like a pair of butterfly wings. Add a glacé cherry to the centre of each cake to finish. Experiment by adding different cake toppings every time you make them. Enjoy!

Crazy Golf

Transform your home into a mini crazy golf course and invite some friends over to play a few rounds.

You Will Need:

* ✻ an umbrella, a broom or a walking stick to use as a golf club
* ✻ a sheet of paper ✻ a saucepan
* ✻ obstacles like boxes, cardboard tubes, CD cases, books, silver baking foil
* ✻ masking tape ✻ sticky tape
* ✻ a small rubber ball – don't use a golf ball as they are too hard to use inside!

SETTING UP THE COURSE

1. You will need plenty of space, so before you begin, check that other members of your family won't need to use the rooms you'll be playing in.

2. Work out a route for each player to follow. It can start in one room and end in another and should involve going under and round furniture, maybe even down stairs. It can pass through doorways – which the ball must go through without touching the door or frame. It can include bouncing the ball off spots on the skirting board marked with masking tape.

3. Mark the beginning of your route with a circle cut from paper and the end of your route with a saucepan into which you must hit the ball to finish.

4. Put away anything fragile from the area surrounding your route to prevent breakages.

5. Put down some obstacles. They could include:

* ✻ Cardboard tubes and boxes with holes cut into the sides that players have to knock the ball through
* ✻ Books to zigzag between
* ✻ Boxes to bounce the ball off in a fixed order
* ✻ Crinkly baking foil laid out flat on the floor.

6. Give the course a trial run to check it, as setting up a good course will involve some trial and error. Change the elements of the course that are too difficult or too easy. Now you are ready to play!

HOW TO PLAY

Each player must gently hit the ball around the course with the 'golf club', negotiating all the obstacles. Write down how many times each player has to hit the ball before it lands in the saucepan.

A penalty point, which counts for three hits, must be added if a player has to pick up the ball and move it if it is trapped.

When everyone has completed the course, add together the number of hits and penalty points for each player. The player with the lowest score wins!

Time For Tea

Teacups at the ready for this party board game! You'll need a dice and some buttons for counters. Roll the dice to start.

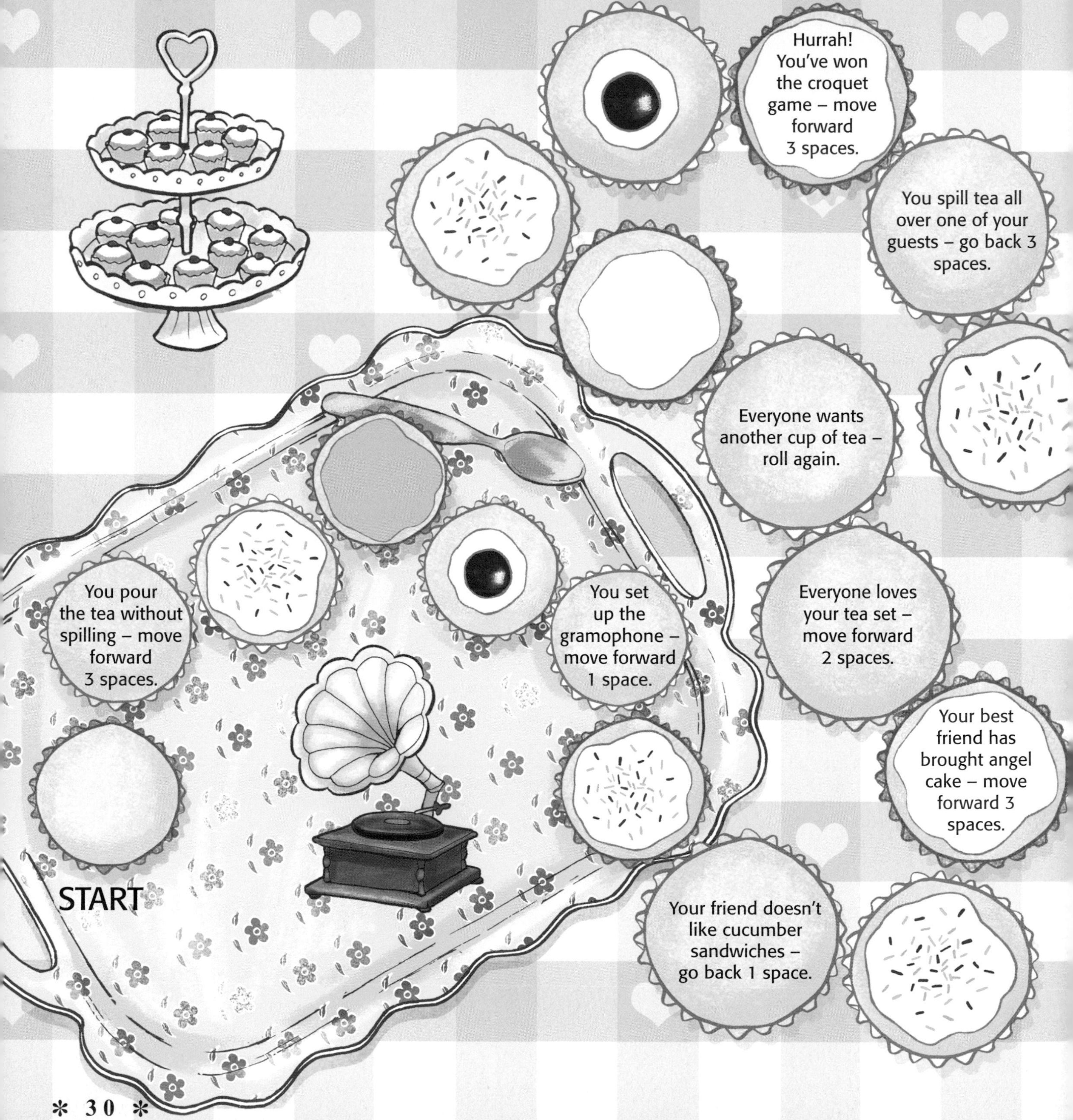

Hurrah! You've won the croquet game – move forward 3 spaces.

You spill tea all over one of your guests – go back 3 spaces.

Everyone wants another cup of tea – roll again.

You pour the tea without spilling – move forward 3 spaces.

You set up the gramophone – move forward 1 space.

Everyone loves your tea set – move forward 2 spaces.

Your best friend has brought angel cake – move forward 3 spaces.

START

Your friend doesn't like cucumber sandwiches – go back 1 space.

You've run out of milk – go back 2 spaces.

There's enough cake for everyone to have a second helping – go forward 1 space.

An uninvited guest turns up – roll an even number to move on.

You suggest a game of Hide and Seek – move forward 2 spaces.

Oh no, the ants have arrived – go back 5 spaces.

You trip over playing Blind Man's Buff – go back 1 space.

Congratulations! You've thrown the best tea party ever!

YOU WIN!

It's too hot to do anything – miss a turn.

Cake time – move forward 3 spaces.

You find a parasol to shade your party from the sun – move forward 1 space.

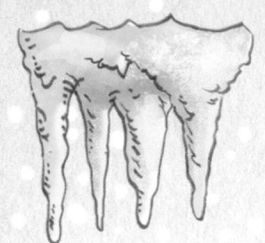
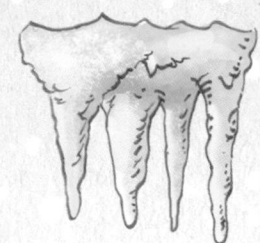

Icecapades

Enter a winter wonderland of puzzles to solve.
Slip and slide to page 60 to check your answers.

WOOLLY WONDERING

Sort the gloves into matching pairs.

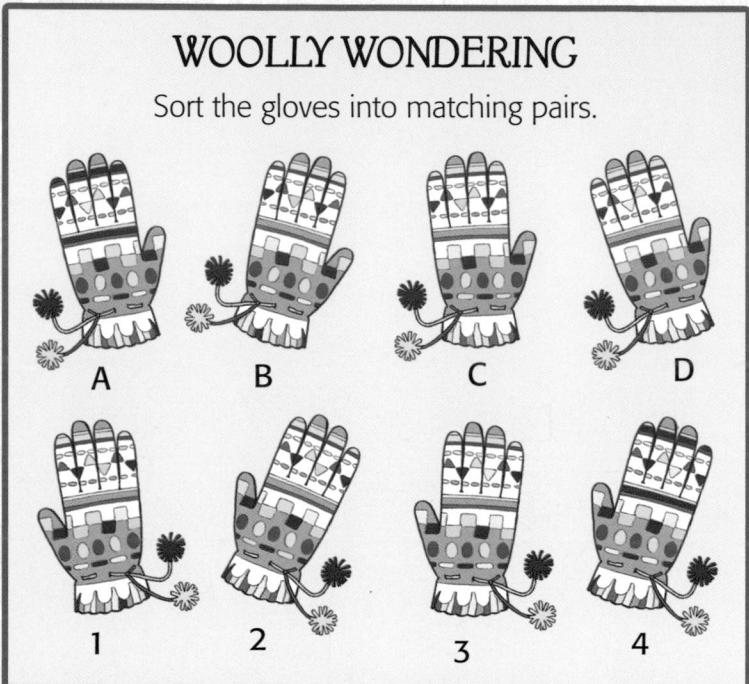

SNOW-DOKU

Complete the grid so that there is a skate, a house, a snowflake and a snowman in each row, column and box of four.

ICY ANAGRAMS

Unscramble the letters to form eight wintry words.

WANNOMS   FWOKNALSE

LECCII   CAVALALAB

STIMENT   BLOBEB TAH

THO OOLTHACCE   TORFS

FIND THE SKATE

Alice has lost her skate. It is not pink. It has red laces and more than one star on the side. Can you help her find it?

A  B  C  D  E  F

SKATE SCRAMBLE

Can you follow the skaters' tracks
to discover which hat belongs to which girl?

Paper Snowflakes

Here's how to make pretty paper snowflakes to decorate your bedroom. You could even make several dozen of them and hang them in your window to cast pretty shadows.

You Will Need:

* plain white or holographic paper cut into squares
* a pencil
* scissors
* glitter glue
* thread

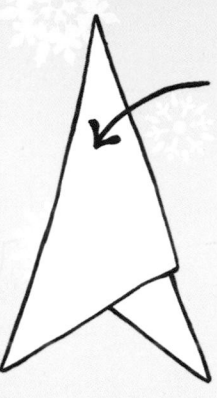

3. Repeat step **2** with the other point so that the shape looks like this.

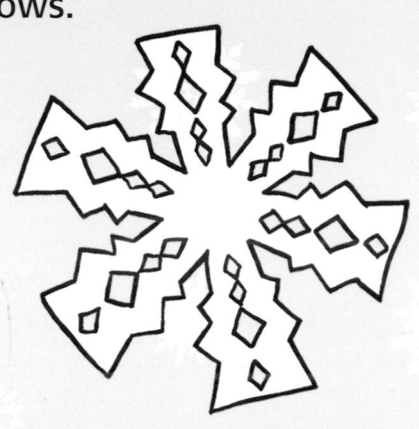

6. Cut along the pencil lines with scissors. Unfold the paper to reveal a beautiful snowflake! Use glitter glue to add some icy finishing touches to your design.

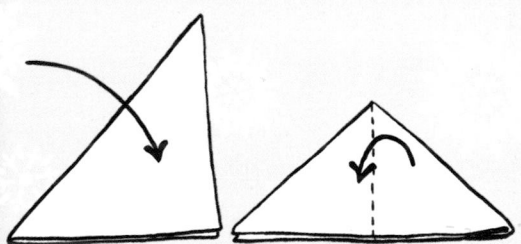

1. Fold the paper in half across the diagonal. Do not unfold the paper but fold it in half again along the long edge.

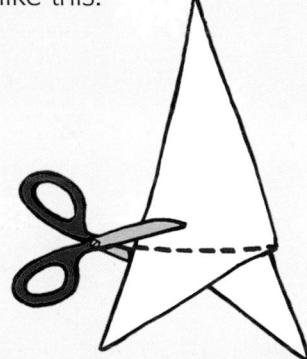

4. Draw a straight line between the two points, and cut both of them off, as shown here.

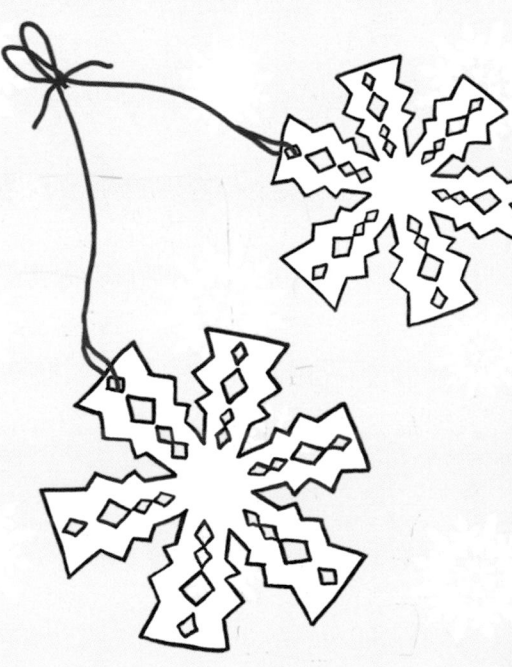

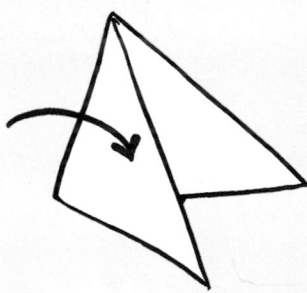

2. Fold one corner about one quarter of the way across the base of your triangle so that it looks like this.

5. Draw zigzags and shapes along the long sides of the triangle. Make sure you aren't going to cut down the whole of one side, as this will make the snowflake come apart.

7. When the glitter glue has dried, tie a piece of thread through one of the holes at the edge of your snowflake, and hang it up wherever you like.

Sensational Seasons

Are you a summer girl or a winter wonder, a spring sweetie or an autumn angel? Follow the flowchart to find out which season suits you best.

START
You prefer chocolate ice cream to sticky toffee pudding.

— YES → More of your clothes are floral than stripy or polka-dotted.

— NO → You know how to knit, or would like to learn.

More of your clothes are floral than stripy or polka-dotted.
— YES → Swimming is your favourite sport.
— NO → You're scared of fireworks.

You know how to knit, or would like to learn.
— NO → You're scared of fireworks.
— YES → You usually prefer hot chocolate to fruit smoothies.

Swimming is your favourite sport.
— NO → You prefer bright colours to pastels.
— YES → You find it quite easy to keep yourself entertained.

You're scared of fireworks.
— YES → You find it quite easy to keep yourself entertained.
— NO → You love putting on fancy dress.

You usually prefer hot chocolate to fruit smoothies.
— NO → You love putting on fancy dress.
— YES → Christmas carols make you happy all year round.

You prefer bright colours to pastels.
— NO → Spring Sweetie
— YES → You thrive on change.

You find it quite easy to keep yourself entertained.
— NO → You thrive on change.
— YES → Secretly, you quite like school.

You love putting on fancy dress.
— NO → Secretly, you quite like school.
— YES → You love spending time with your family.

Christmas carols make you happy all year round.
— NO → You love spending time with your family.
— YES → Winter Wonder

You thrive on change.
— YES → Spring Sweetie
— NO → Summer Girl

Secretly, you quite like school.
— NO → Summer Girl
— YES → Autumn Angel

You love spending time with your family.
— NO → Autumn Angel
— YES → Winter Wonder

Spring Sweetie

You are a bright and hopeful spirit who appreciates the chance to begin anew. You are a bit of a girlie girl, but that doesn't stop you from being quite adventurous too.

Summer Girl

You're a laid-back lady who loves the long, lazy days of summer. You're sweet, sociable and have a calming effect on everyone around you.

Autumn Angel

You are a thoughtful, mellow person, and autumn is your time to shine. You can appreciate beauty in unusual places and you know how to seize each moment.

Winter Wonder

You're a cheery soul who shines most brightly in the winter months. You are loyal, optimistic, and you love special occasions.

Lost And Found

Laura has left some
of her stuff lying around the
house. Can you help her to find it all?

START

BEDROOM

BATHROOM

KITCHEN

LOUNGE

FINISH

In this maze are four of Laura's favourite things: **(1)** her MP3 player, **(2)** her blue teddy bear,

(3) her ballet shoes and **(4)** her charm bracelet. Follow the maze from the start and see if you can find the missing objects in the correct order, ending up in the kitchen. You cannot use the same route twice. The answer is on **page 61**.

Fortune Finder

Unleash your inner psychic and use this fortune teller to predict the future.

 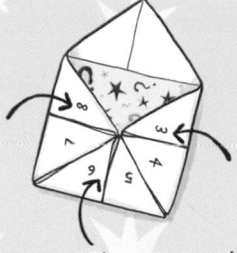 

1. Cut around the fortune finder below. Fold it across the diagonal each way. Place the fortune finder face down and fold the corners so that they meet in the middle, as shown.

2. Turn it over and fold the corners in to the middle once more, as shown.

3. Fold the whole fortune finder in half so that the coloured squares are on the outside, as shown. Unfold, then fold it in half again the other way.

5 — Be nice to someone and your kindness will keep coming back to you.

6 — Someone who holds the key to your future will soon come into your life.

4 — You will soon prove to everyone that you are unstoppable.

1 — You will have a brilliant idea, but you must act on it wisely.

3 — You will achieve what you want, but only by being patient.

8 — Your inner strength will be tested, but you will remain firm.

2 — Only when you understand the past will your future become clear.

1 — Your ability to keep a secret will soon be very important.

HOW TO READ SOMEONE'S FORTUNE

Slip your forefingers and thumbs under the coloured flaps of the fortune finder. Ask a friend to choose a colour. Spell out the colour, opening and closing the fortune finder as you say each letter. Ask them to choose a number inside and open and close the fortune finder the same number of times. Leave it open as you say the final number and ask them to choose another number. Lift the flap to read their fortune!

Dream Decoder

Dreams can be a way for your unconscious to tell you what's really been bugging you. Use the handy guide below to discover what your dreams actually mean.

ACCESSORIES

If you dream about putting on an accessory, it may be that you feel that something is missing in your life.

MUSICAL INSTRUMENTS

Dreaming about musical instruments shows that you are living life to the full and can expect fun times ahead.

CLOTHING

In dreams, clothes represent the way you present yourself to other people. If you dream that you are wearing things you wouldn't normally choose, it means that you are keeping your true self hidden.

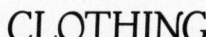

MOBILE PHONES

To dream that you are using a mobile phone shows that you are open to new things. If you dream that you have lost your phone, it might be because you are finding it difficult to tell people how you really feel.

PUPPIES

If you dream about playing with a puppy, it suggests that you are carefree. Dreaming about taking care of a puppy shows that you are reliable and trustworthy.

MAGIC

Dreams about magic suggest that you may benefit from looking at things in a different way, or asking someone else's advice.

CUPCAKES

Dreaming about a cupcake means that you've been thinking too much about a certain problem. Try to take a step back from your worries and focus instead on what you enjoy.

SCISSORS

If you dream about using scissors, you may be feeling unfocused and wanting to get rid of something in your life. It shows that you want to be decisive and take control.

BUTTERFLIES

Dreaming about butterflies shows that you have been changing a lot as a person, but will emerge happier in the end.

COMBS

Dreaming that you are combing your hair suggests that there is a tangle of small problems that you need to sort through.

FLOWERS

In dreams, flowers stand for love and kindness. Seeing them could mean that you need to let your family and friends know how much you really care.

BIKES

If you dream about riding a bike, it probably means that there is a lot going on in your life. Take some time for yourself to make sure that you stay calm and balanced.

Friends Forever?

Ellie, Nicola, Asha and Rachel were the best of friends, but now that they all had to go to different schools, how would they stay close?

'Wow, I can't believe that was actually our last day at Park School!' exclaimed Rachel. The four of them were sitting in Ellie's pink bedroom, surrounded by an impressive array of sandwiches, cakes and sweets.

'I know,' said Asha, helping herself to some lemonade. 'I never thought I'd say this, but I think I'm going to miss it.'

'Still, starting a new school should be interesting,' Nicola chimed in.

'Yes,' sighed Asha, 'but it's not going to be the same now that the four of us will be going to different places.'

'I can't believe my mum won't let me go to the same school as you, Asha,' said Ellie.

'Did you try to persuade her?' Asha asked.

'Yes,' said Ellie. 'But she said we couldn't afford it and that was that.'

'My dad said that there was no point in going to a particular school just to be with my friends,' said Rachel, gloomily. 'He said that in a few months we'd have forgotten all about each other.'

Her three best friends looked deeply shocked.

'But we're going to be best friends forever!' exclaimed Nicola.

'Yes!' affirmed Asha.

'Forever!' echoed Ellie. There was a moment's silence.

'I'm looking forward to learning French,' said Nicola, who was obviously trying to change the subject. 'And there might be some nice people there, maybe even some boys who aren't totally unbearable.'

'Ugh, unlike David Young!' said Ellie. 'That rotten egg prank he played today was disgusting.'

'I know,' said Asha. 'I'm so glad he got into trouble for it.'

'At least none of us are going to the same school as him,' said Nicola brightly.

'I love how you can always see the positive in everything, Nicola,' said Rachel. *'That's what I'm going to miss most about you,'* she thought to herself.

MAKEOVER MAGIC

The four best friends settled down to watch a film. Ellie had chosen a high school comedy about some cheerleaders who were competing with each other over who would get to be prom queen. Although they started out as best friends, they were soon tricking each other and spreading rumours, until finally they had a massive food fight in the school cafeteria. They only made up at the prom when they found out that none of them had been voted queen, and the dreamy captain of the football team brought the nerdiest girl in the school as his date.

'Do you think it'll really be like that at school?' asked Asha.

'I expect so,' said Ellie wisely.

'At least the ending was happy,' said Nicola.

'Let's do our makeovers now,' said Rachel.

'Cool!' said Ellie.

Soon they were busy applying make-up and giving each other manicures and pedicures. Everyone admired the stars Nicola had painted on Asha's nails, Rachel's amazing blended eyeshadow, and the stunning satin bow that transformed Ellie's curls. They gossiped into the night, whispering, giggling and hushing each other after Ellie's dad rather crossly informed them that some people had to go to work in the morning. It must have been about 3 am before they finally started dropping off to sleep.

STRANGE DREAMS

The next day, the sun rose on a beautiful clear morning. Light streamed through the curtains of Ellie's room.

'I love the first day of the holidays,' yawned Nicola.

'Yeah,' said Rachel, 'There are so many possibilities.'

'This is going to sound weird, but I had a really vivid dream last night,' said Asha. 'The four of us were at a concert or something, but we were really old, like 18.'

'That's funny,' said Ellie. 'Because I had a dream that we were all at a wedding. Your wedding, I think, Asha. There were lots of exciting new people there, but the three of us were all in matching dresses because you'd chosen us to be your bridesmaids.'

'In my dream we were really, really old, maybe 80,' said Nicola. 'And we were still having a laugh together.'

'What do I look like with wrinkles?' asked Ellie.

'Better than me,' replied Nicola, hitting her playfully with her pillow.

'Well, in my dream we were the about the same age as we are now,' said Rachel matter-of-factly. 'We were all at a sleepover together –'

'That's not very interesting,' Nicola interrupted. 'Are you sure that that was even a dream?'

'Let me finish,' said Rachel. 'It wasn't just a sleepover, it was a meeting of our sleepover club.'

'A sleepover club?' said Asha.

'Yes,' said Rachel. 'We all decided to meet up for a sleepover at least once a month. Even though we'd found loads of new mates at our new schools, we were all still really close.'

A NEW BEGINNING

'Do you think dreams really do come true?' asked Ellie quietly.

'I think people can make their dreams come true,' said Asha. 'And a good idea is a good idea.'

'Let's do it!' said Nicola excitedly. 'We can be sleepover sisters!'

Asha quickly poured them all a glass of lemonade.

'To the Sleepover Sisters,' said Ellie, Rachel, Nicola and Asha together, raising their plastic cups. 'Best friends forever!'

Sleepover Sisters

Nadia and Claire are trying on different outfits at a sleepover. Can you spot the twelve differences between the two bedrooms? The answers are on page 61.

Cheesecake Brownies

These chocolate brownies make an indulgently rich treat. The secret to baking brownies is to watch them carefully to make sure that they don't overcook. Slightly underdone brownies are fabulously fudgy.

1. Preheat the oven to 180 °C/Gas mark 4.

2. Line a 20 by 30 cm tin with foil.

3. Half fill a saucepan with water. Place a bowl in the pan so that it sits above the water level. Add the butter and chocolate to the bowl and heat the water to melt the ingredients.

4. Beat the eggs in a bowl with half of the sugar and the vanilla essence.

5. Once the chocolate mixture has cooled slightly, add it to the egg mixture, then add the flour and salt. Mix well.

6. In a separate bowl, blend the rest of the sugar with the cream cheese.

You Will Need:

* ✳ 125 g unsalted butter
* ✳ 125 g dark chocolate
* ✳ 2 eggs
* ✳ 300 g caster sugar
* ✳ 1 teaspoon vanilla essence
* ✳ 75 g plain flour
* ✳ 1 teaspoon salt
* ✳ 200 g cream cheese

7. Spoon alternating blobs of chocolate and cream cheese mixture into the lined tin. Swirl the mixtures with a skewer to create a marbled effect. Make sure you don't mix them too much.

8. Bake in the oven for 30 minutes or until a skewer inserted into the centre comes out clean. Set aside in the tin for 1 hour to cool. Cut into squares and serve with ice cream.

WARNING:
Ask an adult to help you when you use the oven and the stove.

Talk To The Hand

Here's how to communicate with your friends without even speaking.

A-OK

Use this hand gesture to tell people that everything is fine. Just don't use it if you're in Italy, Germany, Brazil or Spain, as you would be insulting them!

WELL DONE

The thumbs up is a popular hand gesture people often use to congratulate each other. Be careful though, as it's quite rude in Latin America, Greece, Iran and Saudi Arabia.

HIGH FIVE!

Great for congratulating friends on a job well done. If you're feeling particularly adventurous, you might like to try low fives, side fives and clapping above your heads for ceiling fives.

SHE'S CRAZY

Useful for telling a friend she's being silly, or pointing out someone who's acting strangely. A bit confusing in Argentina, where it means 'You've got a phone call.'

DID YOU KNOW?

It is thought that people used signs and gestures before spoken language developed.

The first set sign language was invented 250 years ago in France to help deaf children in school. Today, people in different countries sign to each other in different languages. Someone who knows British Sign Language would still have to learn different signs for some words to talk to an American.

Even in the same country, signs can vary slightly from place to place, just as there are different spoken accents in different towns.

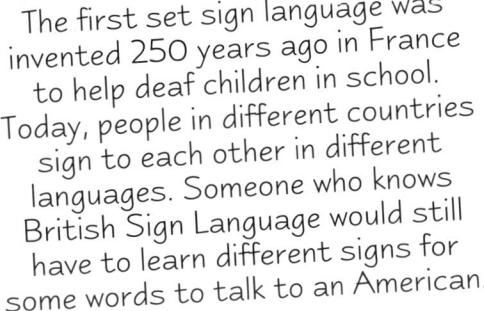
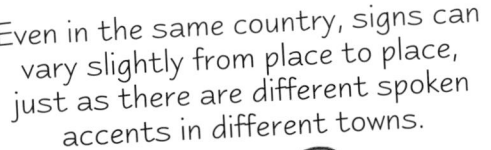

EXPLODING FISTBUMP

Yo! Greet your homies by tapping your clenched fists together.

Hanging Heart

Here's how to make a cool heart-shaped photo frame. Hang it in your room or give it to a friend to remind her of all the great times you've spent together.

You Will Need:

* ✳ Plain white A4 paper ✳ Scissors
* ✳ 1 packet of polymer clay in pink or red, available from craft shops
* ✳ A rolling pin ✳ A table knife
* ✳ Kitchen foil ✳ A toothpick
* ✳ A photo of you and your friend
* ✳ PVA glue
* ✳ A short (roughly 20 cm) length of sparkly string or wool

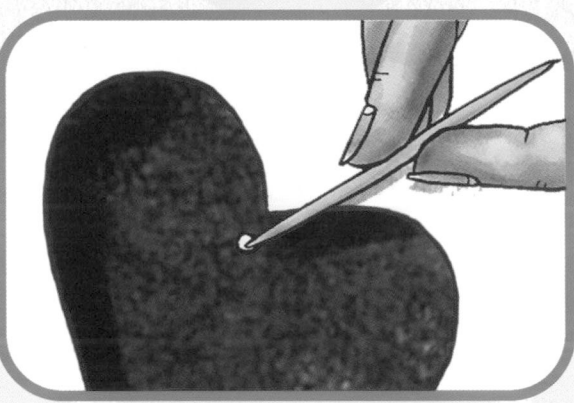

2. Take about a third of the modelling clay to make the back of your photo frame. Warm and soften the clay in your hands, then roll it out using a rolling pin. Place the template over the clay and use a blunt knife to cut out the shape. Make a hole as shown. If you like you can also use the toothpick to write a special message on the back of the clay heart.

3. Once you are happy with your clay heart, place it on a sheet of kitchen foil on a baking tray. Cut out the smaller heart shape that you traced earlier. Don't worry about ruining the outer heart, as you won't need it again. Place the smaller paper heart in the middle of your clay heart. Make sure that it is on the opposite side to the writing, if you have added any.

4. Divide the remaining clay into small balls. You can make as many as you like, but try to keep them between 1 and 1.5 cm in diameter.

WARNING:
Ask an adult to help you when you use the oven.

1. Use a piece of plain paper to trace the two heart shapes above, then cut around the outside edge of the larger one. This is your template.

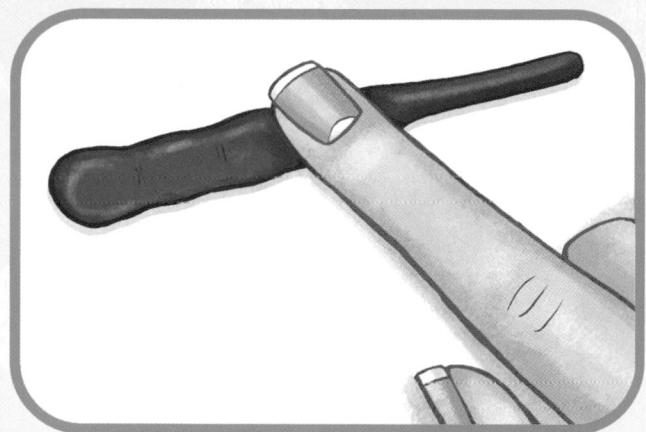

5. Take one of the balls of clay and roll it into a long sausage-shape. Squash it with your fingers so that you end up with a long, flat piece of clay.

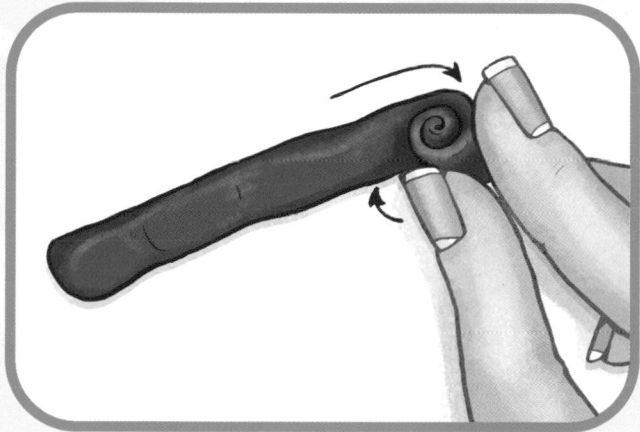

6. Now roll the clay up from one end to create a coil. Pinch it together on one side to make a rosebud.

7. Carefully but firmly push the sides of the rosebud onto the outer edge of the frame, using the position of the small paper heart to help you. Repeat stages **5** and **6** until you have completely covered the outer edge of the frame. Make sure you don't press the top of the bud, or you'll lose the shape.

8. Once you are happy with the frame, remove the paper heart and put the tray in the oven, following the instructions on the clay packet. Check with an adult first that it's all right for you to use the oven.

9. Position the small paper heart on the photograph of you and your friend, so that your faces are in the centre. Draw around the heart, then cut out the picture.

10. Once the clay heart is cool, use the glue to stick the photo in place in the centre of the frame. Thread the sparkly yarn through the hole and tie it in a loop. Hang up the ornament wherever you like, or wrap it up and give it to your best friend.

* JUST FOR GIRLS *

Treasure Trail

Brush up on your map reading with the guide below and then use your skills
to follow the clues and find the hidden treasure in the map opposite.
Turn to page 61 for the answer.

MAP-READING ESSENTIALS

Symbols key – In the bottom right corner of
the map you will see a key that shows you what all
the symbols mean. These can vary from map to map,
so always double-check what each one means.

Compass Points – A good map will have a
symbol to show you which way is north. This
will help you find the right direction when you
are travelling.

Number co-ordinates – Most maps are
broken up into a grid of squares. The quickest way to
direct someone to a precise place on a map is by
using the numbers along the sides. These are the
co-ordinates. The numbers along the top or bottom
are always given first, then the numbers down the
side. The phrase 'along the corridor and up the stairs'
will help you remember the order. For example, the
co-ordinates of the cupcake are **(1, 9)** while the bow
is at **(8, 9)** and the kite is at **(10, 3)**.

Scale – It is important that every good map has a
scale. This tells you the distance that the map
represents, and helps you work out how far you will
have to travel. On this map, to cover one square, you
would have to travel one kilometre in real life.

Contour Lines – The red lines on this map are
are called contour lines that join points of the same
height. They are marked with a number that shows
you the height above sea level. Contour lines that are
close together show you that the land is steep, while
widely spaced lines show that it is quite flat.

START THE TREASURE HUNT

The six clues are written out below. The trouble is,
someone has jumbled up the order in which they
should be followed. To find the hidden loot, follow
the map to direct you to the letter of the next clue,
and finally to the treasure's secret hiding place.
The first clue is hidden at the museum.

A Follow the lane to the top of Hawthorne Hill

B Run to square **(13, 5)**

C Find the strawberry patch by the river

D Skip to the picnic site to the south of
Crackley Wood

E Jump to square **(5, 9)**

F Travel one kilometre north of the fairground

Write where you think the treasure is hidden here:

Poodle Parlour Palaver

Sarah loves puppies, but her mum thinks they are too much of a handful. After the dogs run riot in Miss Miller's poodle parlour, how can Sarah convince her otherwise? The answers to the puzzle are on page 61.

'That's the most gorgeous puppy ever,' said Sarah wistfully.

It was her fourth week helping out Miss Miller at Doggie Tails, the local poodle parlour, and a woman had just come in with a beautiful golden puppy. Sarah desperately wanted a puppy of her own, but her mum was very strict about animals. She said that pets were too much fuss and that anyway Sarah could always play with her friends' dogs, cats, rats and gerbils.

'Hello, I'm Mrs Bloom,' said the woman with the puppy. 'I made an appointment for Buster. I'd like you to make sure he looks extra-nice.'

'Of course,' said Miss Miller, who was grooming three very elegant poodles. 'Our usual doggie stylist Kara is off sick today, but Sarah will do an excellent job.'

'Fine,' said Mrs Bloom. 'Shall I come back in a couple of hours and pick him up?'

'That would be perfect,' said Miss Miller.

LEFT IN CHARGE

Buster licked playfully at her fingers as Sarah carefully lifted him into the special bath. She directed the hose over Buster's shiny fur until it was soaked through and squeezed out some mild dog shampoo from the big bottle. She massaged the shampoo in gentle circles, making sure that every inch of his fur was completely clean. Buster seemed to like the bubbles.

'I'm just going out for some milk,' said Miss Miller, who had almost finished grooming the poodles. 'You will be all right down here on your own for a moment, won't you?'

'Yes, of course,' said Sarah.

Everything was fine for a while. Sarah rinsed the shampoo from Buster's fur. Suddenly a cat, which must have crept in through the back door, jumped on to the side table and knocked over a bottle. The poodles, who had been waiting patiently for Miss Miller's return, were startled by the noise. They barked madly and chased after the cat, tipping soapy water everywhere. Gramps, a big brown mongrel, rushed in and started jumping on the tables. Buster gave a cheeky bark and shook himself off, spraying the entire room, before joining the doggy rampage as the cat sped out of the shop leaving chaos in its wake.

WHAT A MESS!

There was soap and water everywhere and the dogs showed no sign of quietening down. Sarah's heart rose in her throat. She was sure that if Miss Miller saw her shop in this state she would never let her come to Doggie Tails again.

Sarah took a deep breath and tried not to panic. She found some extra leads and secured the poodles. Buster, though still excited, was getting quite tired, so it was easy to put him on a lead, too. Gramps was the hardest to catch. He ran in circles when Sarah tried to chase him, diving under the furniture and speeding past her. Sarah pretended to ignore him and, when he trotted curiously up to her, she pounced. Then she grabbed the towels and began cleaning up the mess.

'Sorry about that!' said Miss Miller cheerfully, when she came back an hour later. 'I had to go to the bank, too. Town was really busy today.'

Sarah breathed an inward sigh of relief. Miss Miller didn't seem to have noticed a thing.

Then Miss Miller said, 'Why are these towels wet?'

'I'm ever so sorry, Miss Miller,' confessed Sarah

right away. 'I did my best to tidy up afterwards, but the dogs went a little, er, wild after you left. You don't want me to leave, do you?'

'Leave? Of course not! You've got a way with animals. It was unfair of me to leave you alone with five dogs.'

Sarah beamed. 'Thanks! I love helping out here.'

'Those dogs,' Miss Miller said, tutting fondly. 'They are so naughty when they are together. I just can't believe how efficiently you managed to clean up. Why, the place hasn't been this clean in years!'

Sarah's mum stepped into the shop to just hear the end of this, and faked a comical look of surprise.

'It's a pity the same can't be said about Sarah's room,' she joked.

'Mum!' said Sarah, embarrassed.

'Don't worry, darling, I'm just having a chat with Miss Miller,' her mother said. 'You carry on here.'

A SURPRISE IN STORE

Sarah carefully dried Buster off and combed his golden fur. She had just finished tying a special ribbon around Buster's neck when Mrs Bloom walked in.

'Don't you look lovely, Buster?' said Mrs Bloom. She sighed. 'I'm sure you won't be waiting too long at the animal shelter. Someone is bound to want to adopt you soon.'

'Adopt him?' Sarah blurted out.

'Yes,' said Mrs Bloom, sadly. 'I bought Buster as a birthday present for my daughter, Juliet, but we didn't realise that she was allergic to dogs. She loves him dearly, but we can't keep him.'

'She must be so sad!' Sarah said.

'Yes,' said Mrs Bloom. 'She was afraid that nobody would want him and he'd be all alone at the shelter, so I promised to take him to the poodle parlour before I dropped him off. He needs to look his best.'

'We could give him a home,' Sarah's mum offered.

'Really?' said Sarah and Mrs Bloom in unison.

'Yes, of course,' said Sarah's mum. 'I think Sarah has proved that she would be a very responsible dog owner. Besides, he is very cute.'

'Thanks Mum!' exclaimed Sarah. 'I'll take really good care of him.'

'Juliet will be so glad that Buster is going to such a good home,' said Mrs Bloom.

'Would she like to come and see him?' said Sarah. 'Or would it make her allergies worse?'

'I think she'd love a quick visit,' said Mrs Bloom, as Buster gave a woof of approval and scampered around the shop.

'Just one thing,' said Sarah's mum sternly. 'We are taking Buster to some obedience training sessions!'

Hidden in the picture below there are three leads, five collars and ten doggie treats. Can you help Sarah find them all?

Which City?

Are you best suited to a dynamic New York lifestyle, or a more relaxed existence amid the boutiques, cafés and galleries of Paris? Choose the answers that best describe you to discover your ideal city.

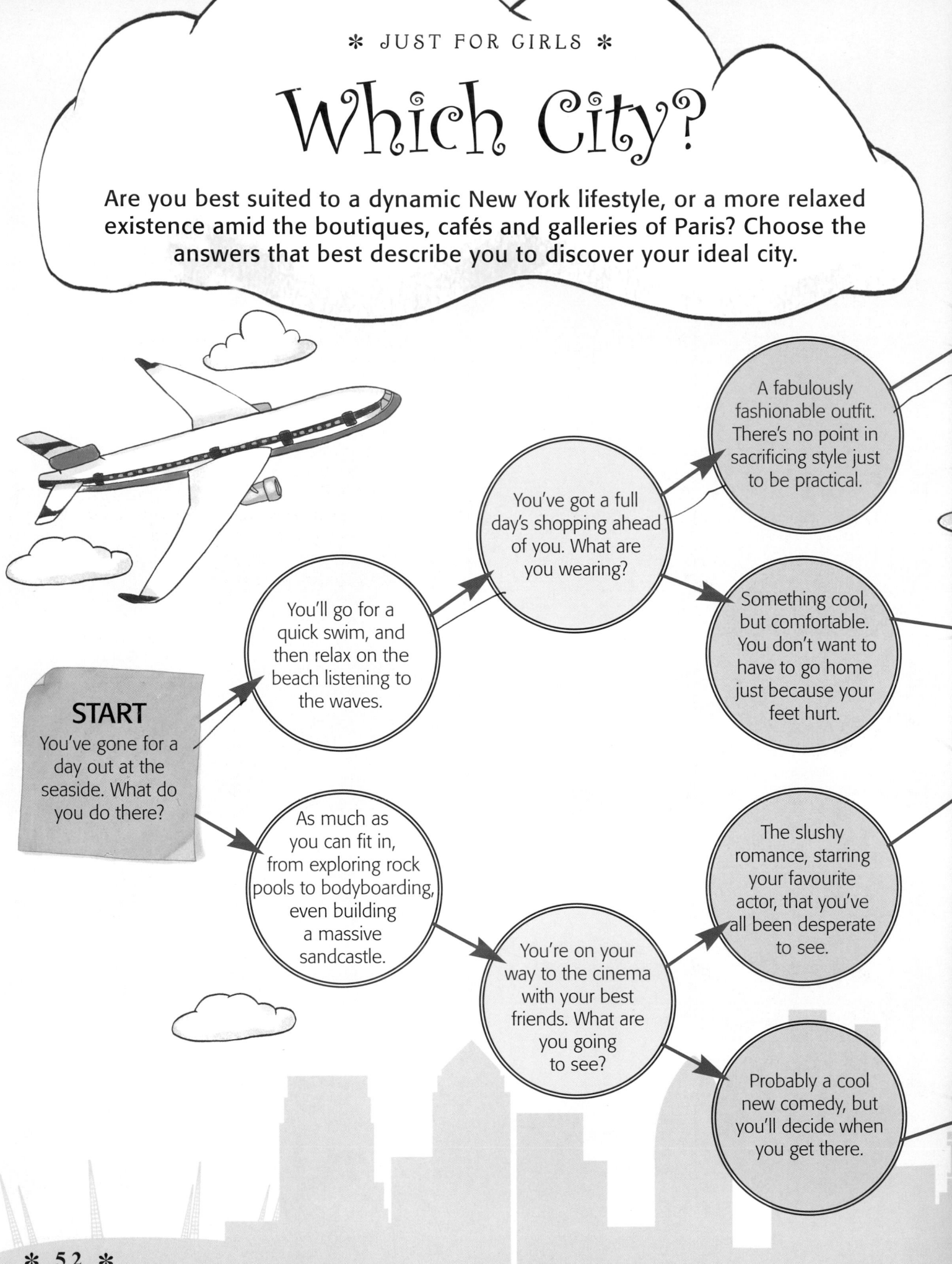

START
You've gone for a day out at the seaside. What do you do there?

You'll go for a quick swim, and then relax on the beach listening to the waves.

As much as you can fit in, from exploring rock pools to bodyboarding, even building a massive sandcastle.

You've got a full day's shopping ahead of you. What are you wearing?

A fabulously fashionable outfit. There's no point in sacrificing style just to be practical.

Something cool, but comfortable. You don't want to have to go home just because your feet hurt.

You're on your way to the cinema with your best friends. What are you going to see?

The slushy romance, starring your favourite actor, that you've all been desperate to see.

Probably a cool new comedy, but you'll decide when you get there.

You're packing for a long journey. What do you take to keep yourself entertained on the trip?

A novel to read and a notebook in case you want to doodle or write something.

Lots of magazines and an MP3 player full of your top tunes.

PARIS

Paris would be your perfect city as you are charming, cultured and sophisticated. You're a chilled and social sort of person who would spend as much time relaxing in bistros and cafés as shopping and visiting art galleries.

LONDON

London's variety would suit you down to the ground. From Camden Market to the fanciest shops in Knightsbridge, and the thronging crowds at Piccadilly Circus to the calm oasis of Hampstead Heath, you'd love the city's many faces.

Your family are going out for a meal, and you get to pick the restaurant. Where do you go?

Somewhere new and different. You'd love to try Lebanese food ... or maybe Mexican, Thai, or Ethiopian ...

Your favourite Italian eatery. You know their menu off by heart – you just can't beat their pizzas and gelato.

NEW YORK

You've got a real sense of fun and would be right at home in New York, the city that never sleeps. You'd never run out of things to do, from watching a musical on Broadway to buying yummy bagels or visiting the fair at Coney Island.

Your birthday is coming up, and you're planning a special outing with your friends. What do you want to do?

You just want to do something fun that gives you plenty of time to chat, like ten-pin bowling and a sleepover.

You're dying to have a go at something you wouldn't normally do, like paintballing or skiing on an indoor slope.

BEIJING

You're an adventurous lady who would love buzzing Beijing. Whether you're taking tea on the rooftops overlooking the Forbidden City or exploring the treasures of the Silk Market, the city's fusion of past and present would be endlessly exciting.

Around the World

There are many unusual traditions in the world, but one of these is completely made up. Can you work out which one? Check your answer on page 61.

MEXICO

In early November, people in Mexico celebrate the Day of the Dead to make peace with death and honour those who have died. Families decorate graves with tealights and marigolds, build altars in their homes, and make their dead relatives' favourite foods. People make skull masks and toy skeletons and eat breads and candies shaped like skulls.

AUSTRIA

The Schnitzel Dance is an Austrian tradition dating back to the sixteenth century. Every year on the 29th September, boys and girls gather in traditional costumes. They link arms and dance around a large plate of schnitzel, a type of pork coated in breadcrumbs. When the dance is over, everyone shares the schnitzel, and the party lasts all evening.

CHINA

Chinese New Year is celebrated between the 21st January and 20th February. Houses are thoroughly spring cleaned about ten days before the first new moon of the year and New Year's Eve is reserved for family celebrations. The next day, families give each other red envelopes of money and eat prosperity cake and sticky rice balls.

There are dances and fireworks in the two weeks running up to the Lantern Festival at the full moon, a night when colourful lanterns light up the houses.

WALES

In Wales, there is a traditional poetry and music competition called the Eisteddfod (pronounced 'ice-teth-*vod*'). Its roots go back to medieval competitions between court poets and harpists. They take place in towns and villages throughout the year and there is also a larger Royal National Eisteddfod every summer.

SPAIN

A form of music, singing and dance called flamenco originates from southern Spain. The singer's song usually tells a story about being part of a culture separate from the rest of Spain. Men perform intricate footwork, while ladies wear fancy ruffled dresses and emphasize the hands and upper body as they dance.

Market Maze

Isabelle is on her way to a birthday party, but first she needs to go to the cake stand, party stall and clothes stall, in that order. Can you help her visit the shops and find the exit without using the same route twice? The solution is on page 61.

START

PARTY SUPPLIES

CAKES

CLOTHES

EXIT

Be A Fantastic Friend

Follow these fantastic tips to be the best friend anyone could ask for.

STYLE

✳ If your friend asks for your opinion on what she's wearing, she obviously really admires your sense of style. Even if you think she looks terrible, don't tell her that but instead try to gently steer her towards a look that will suit her better.

✳ A great way to help your friend change her style is to hold a swap shop. Bring round all the clothes you don't want any more and trade them for some of her unwanted items. Who knows, you could end up with some great stuff!

BIRTHDAYS

✳ Write down your friends' birthdays in a special book so that you never forget them.

✳ Note down your friend's specific likes and dislikes, so that when her birthday comes round you have no problem picking out the perfect present.

PROBLEMS

✳ If your friend comes to you with a problem, be honest but tactful about her situation. Don't be upset if your friend doesn't take your advice, but support her in whatever decision she finally makes. Don't say, 'I told you so,' if it doesn't work out for the best.

✳ Offer your friend a shoulder to cry on when she's feeling down.

✳ If your friend has been going through a difficult time lately, why not make a Friendship Emergency Kit? Fill a shoe box with lots of her favourite things and put in a note explaining why you think she rocks.

SECRETS

✳ If your friend has entrusted you with a secret, you owe it to her to keep it quiet. Don't tell another person. If you are struggling, try telling your dog, cat, or even your teddy bear. It'll get the secret off your chest and they're unlikely to spread it across the whole school!

✳ Pay attention to what your friend says, as well as filling her in on all your latest gossip. If you go on about yourself all the time, she is less likely to tell you when something important comes up.

Horoscopes

What do the stars have to say about your future?

	ARIES	TAURUS	GEMINI	CANCER
	March 21st to April 20th	April 21st to May 21st	May 22nd to June 21st	June 22nd to July 22nd
Lucky Colour	Red	Green	Turquoise	Baby pink
Lucky Animal	Fox	Chinchilla	Hamster	Otter
About You	There's absolutely no stopping you! You are outgoing and enthusiastic. Your fiery personality means you can be quite competitive and you're always on the lookout for a new adventure.	You are a charming person who wears her heart on her sleeve. You like luxury and hate doing without your creature comforts. You are hard-working, patient and you'd never let a friend down.	You are quick-witted and always on the go. You're a bit of a chatterbox and can keep others entertained with ease. You get bored quite easily, but this means that you adapt well to change.	You have a powerful imagination which you are quite shy of sharing with others. Once you feel close to someone, you are an attentive and loyal friend. You also have a strong sense of intuition.
Your Coming Year	This will be a busy and exciting year for you. Don't push people away as you go after your dreams. Show friends that you love them. A mature attitude will make people more willing to listen to you.	This year you will be full of original and brilliant ideas. Just make sure other people don't take your jokes too seriously. Taking the opportunity to help a friend in need will bring you closer together.	Your patience may be challenged early in the year, but stick with things and you will soon see the rewards. You may be slightly annoyed by certain restrictions, but they will help in the long run.	This is a good year for expanding your horizons and meeting new friends. You may get the chance to travel this year, which you should seize. There's time to do everything, so don't forget your family either.
Lucky Objects	• Amber jewellery • Polkadot dresses • Diamond • Honeysuckle • Plums	• Silver rings • Stripy jumpers • Emerald • Foxgloves • Pears	• Charm bracelets • Red shoes • Tiger's eye • Lavender • Passionfruit	• Heart necklaces • Pink tops • Pearl • Lilies • Watermelons

	LEO	VIRGO	LIBRA	SCORPIO
	July 23rd to August 23rd	August 24th to September 22nd	September 23rd to October 23rd	October 24th to November 22nd
Lucky Colour	Gold	Dark blue	Baby blue	Deep pink
Lucky Animal	Pony	Puppy	Gerbil	Owl
About You	Drama-queen alert! You are outgoing, generous and creative, and love being at the centre of things. You can be a bit bossy, but your friends know that's how you show you care.	You are a smart and practical lady who's got life fairly sussed. You work hard but can be a bit too modest about your achievements. Friends and family love your sweet nature and sensible advice.	You are outgoing, warm-hearted and have a lot of charm. You're clever but can be a bit gullible. You're good at sorting out quarrels and you have a wonderfully sociable and laid-back attitude.	You're quite a deep person and your intuition is usually spot on. You live for each moment, and people find you irresistible. You are quite emotional, but you like to keep things private.
Your Coming Year	Many of your dreams will come true this year as you meet new people and try new things. Your strong sense of justice will be tested later on, but you should trust yourself to do the right thing.	You will become more confident, so use the opportunity to do new things and stretch yourself. You may have some difficult decisions to make, so don't be afraid to share your worries.	You will be very busy, so make sure you pace yourself. Your friends are important to you, so give them the attention they deserve. However, don't do things just to get something in return.	This is a great year to get creative. You're determined to achieve your potential, but this will be easier if you take time to relax and think about things. It's best to sort out small problems before they grow.
Lucky Objects	• Friendship bracelets • Bright cardigans • Ruby • Sunflowers • Oranges	• Gold rings • Flowery dresses • Peridot • Lily-of-the-valley • Strawberries	• Sparkly necklaces • Pastel tops • Sapphire • Violets • Grapes	• Silver bangles • Black skirts • Opal • Geraniums • Bananas

	SAGITTARIUS	CAPRICORN	AQUARIUS	PISCES
	November 23rd to December 21st	December 22nd to January 20th	January 21st to February 18th	February 19th to March 20th
Lucky Colour	Purple	White	Silver	Sea green
Lucky Animal	Kitten	Swallow	Duckling	Dolphin
About You	You are intelligent and thoughtful, and always say what you think. You have lots of energy and enjoy new challenges. You're good at looking on the bright side and adapting to new situations.	You are ambitious, wise, and tend to keep yourself to yourself. You know what you want to do, and you are good at making it happen. You're not afraid of a little hard work if it helps you reach your goals.	You are kind and creative and your friends know they can come to you for honest advice. You don't worry too much about what others think. You're just as happy on your own as with a crowd of people.	You have the soul of an artist. Sensitive and imaginative, you care deeply about the people you love. You're a bit of a dreamer, which means you can get a bit lost in your own world.
Your Coming Year	A lot is changing for you, so be ready to embrace new things. Remember to make time for old friends – even when your life gets busy. You will also need to be ready to stand up for causes you believe in.	The year will be filled with good fortune. Your hard work will pay off, but you need to give it a chance to happen. Just don't forget your friends and family when things are going well.	You will discover a new closeness with a friend you don't know well. This year holds many new challenges, so don't be too independent, refuse to take advice or try to be different just for the sake of it.	This will be a great year for you, so make the most of every day. It's a good time to use your artistic talents, so don't keep putting things off. Remember, your gut feelings are usually right.
Lucky Objects	• Chunky pendants • Furry boots • Topaz • Dandelions • Blueberries	• Pearl jewellery • Plaid shirts • Turquoise • Pansies • Peaches	• Gold bracelets • Floaty skirts • Aquamarine • Orchids • Apples	• Thumb rings • Printed dresses • Moonstone • Waterlilies • Melons

Answers

PAGES 12-13

Beauty Mindbuster: A daily bath in milk for soft skin

Pyramid Puzzler

Sneaky Scarabs: C and E

King Tut's Tomb

Sphinx Sudoku

Riddle Me This:
1. An echo   2. Tomorrow   3. A secret
4. A keyhole   5. Silence

PAGE 24 Behind the Scenes

PAGE 25 Movie Magic

1. b 2. a 3. a 4. b 5. c 6. b 7. c 8. a 9. c 10. b

PAGE 27 Ballet Boggler

PAGES 32-33

Woolly Wondering: A and 4, B and 1, C and 2, D and 3

Icy Anagrams: Snowman   Icicle   Mittens
Hot Chocolate   Snowflake   Balaclava   Bobble Hat   Frost

Find The Skate: E

Skate Scramble

Snow-Doku

PAGE 36 Lost and Found

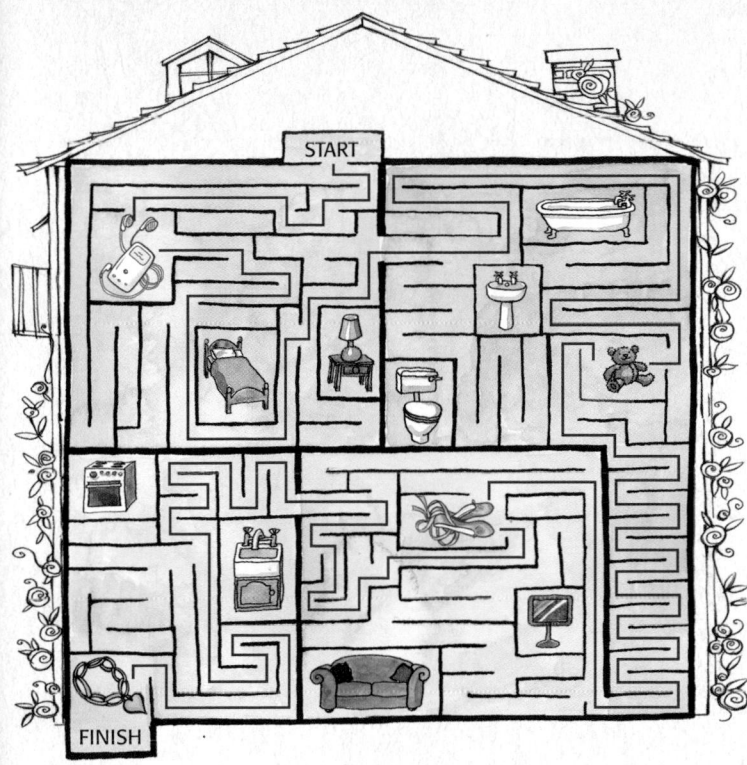

PAGES 48-49

E, A, F, C, D, B

The treasure is hidden at the castle.

PAGE 51 Poodle Parlour Palaver

PAGE 54 Around the World

The Austrian Schnitzel Dance is the false story.

PAGES 42-43 Sleepover Sisters

PAGE 55 Market Maze